Galileo: Science & Faith

by
Dr William E Carroll

*All booklets are published thanks
to the generous support of the members
of the Catholic Truth Society*

ignatius
press · CATHOLIC
TRUTH SOCIETY

LIGHTHOUSE
CATHOLIC MEDIA
A NOT FOR PROFIT CORPORATION

CATHOLIC TRUTH SOCIETY
PUBLISHERS TO THE HOLY SEE

Contents

Icon of Modernity

There are few images of the modern world more powerful than that of the humbled Galileo, kneeling before the cardinals of the Inquisition, being forced to admit that the Earth did not move. The story is a familiar one: that Galileo represents science's fighting to free itself from the clutches of blind faith, biblical literalism, and superstition. In such a narrative, Galileo has the unique privilege of ushering in the modern world, both in terms of his scientific achievements and in his establishing the proper relationship between science and sacred scripture. The specter of the Catholic Church's condemnation of Galileo continues to occupy a prominent place in the modern world's understanding of the relationship between religion and science. A few anecdotal incidents can help make this point. On the occasion of the publication, in March 1987, of the Church's condemnation of *in vitro* fertilisation, surrogate motherhood, and fetal experimentation, there appeared a page of cartoons in one of Rome's major newspapers, *La Repubblica*, with the headline: "*In Vitro Veritas*". In one of the cartoons, two bishops are standing next to a telescope, and in the distant night sky, in addition to Saturn and the Moon, there are dozens of test-tubes. One bishop turns to the other, who is in front of the telescope, and asks: "*This* time what should we do? Should we look or not?" The historical reference to Galileo was clear. In fact, at a press conference at the Vatican, Cardinal Josef Ratzinger was asked whether he thought the Church's response to the new biology would not result in another 'Galileo affair'. The Cardinal smiled, perhaps realising the persistent power - at least in the popular imagination - of the story of Galileo's encounter with the Inquisition more than three hundred and fifty years before. The Vatican office of which Cardinal Ratzinger was then the head, the Congregation for the Doctrine of the Faith, is the direct successor to the Holy, Roman and Universal Inquisition into Heretical Depravity.

Throughout his pontificate, John Paul II expressed a lively interest in the relationship between science and faith. A medal struck by the Vatican in 2003 to commemorate the four-hundreth anniversary of the founding of the Pontifical Academy of Sciences is instructive in this regard. The Pontifical Academy traces its provenance to the Lincean Academy, established in 1603; Galileo was its most famous member. The commemorative medal depicts Pope John Paul in conversation with Galileo. Next to Galileo there is a representation of the universe as he described it, with six planets revolving about the Sun. On the obverse of the medal we find the words from the opening of Genesis referring to God's creation of light (and an artistic representation of this act) as well as the phrase, '*fidei rationisque*' (of faith and reason), calling to mind the Pope's famous encyclical, *Fides et Ratio*.

The Galileo Commission

In October 1992, eleven years before the appearance of the medal, John Paul II appeared before the Pontifical Academy of Sciences to accept formally the findings of a commission of historical, scientific, and theological inquiry into the treatment of Galileo by the Inquisition: a commission which he established in the early 1980s. The Pope noted that the theologians of the Inquisition who condemned Galileo failed to distinguish properly between particular interpretations of the Bible and questions which in fact pertained to scientific investigation.

The Pope also observed that one of the unfortunate consequences of the condemnation of Galileo was that it had been used to reinforce the myth of an incompatibility between faith and science. That such a myth was alive and well was immediately apparent in the way the press described the event in the Vatican. The headline on the front page of *The New York Times* was representative:

"After 350 Years, Vatican Says Galileo Was Right: It Moves." The story referred to "one of the Church's most infamous wrongs - the persecution of the Italian astronomer and physicist for proving the Earth moves about the Sun". The story also claimed that "the dispute between the Church and Galileo has long stood as one of history's great emblems of conflict between reason and dogma, science and faith."

It is not surprising that *The New York Times* would perpetuate one of the more persistent myths concerning Galileo and the Inquisition. Celebrations of the values of modernity are characteristic of much of the secular media, and the legend of Galileo is surely one of the constitutive myths of the modern world. It is a story which has come to characterise our understanding of the origins of modernity. A related feature of the legend, which makes it even more persuasive, is the view of Galileo the scientist, breaking with the scientific views of Aristotle, and thereby helping to lay the foundations of modern science.

The La Sapienza Affair

The events of 1992 had a strange echo in Rome in January 2008 when Pope Benedict XVI cancelled his planned speech at the University of Rome's La Sapienza campus. A group of faculty members and students protested the invitation to the Pope to speak, at first because of the need, so it was argued, to keep faith and religion out of the halls of the academy, and then, more specifically, because of remarks the Pope had made in a speech in 1990 about the Galileo Affair. In reporting on these events in Britain, the BBC contrasted Pope John Paul's admission that the Church had erred in her treatment of Galileo with then Cardinal Ratzinger's 1990 speech in which he quoted the philosopher of science, Paul Feyerabend, who maintained that the Inquisition's treatment of Galileo was "reasonable and just". In fact, the BBC, in the same vein as *The New York Times* in 1992, observed that Pope John Paul had formally and officially acknowledged that the Earth moved!

Cardinal Ratzinger, however, did not endorse Feyerabend's historical judgment so much as reflect on the fact that some scholars had come to see dangers in modern science and technology. As he has done since becoming Pope, he warned against identifying reason only with what science affirms. In 1990 he was addressing what he described as increasing attention in scholarly circles to the limits of science and the criteria which it must observe. He noted that emblematic of this new intellectual climate were the questions that were being asked about the Galileo Affair. Rather than see Galileo as a victim of 'mediaeval obscurantism' and of an attempt to stifle science, some scholars were maintaining

that the Church at the time of Galileo, in Feyerabend's
words, "was much more faithful to reason than Galileo
himself, and also took into consideration the ethical and
social consequences of Galileo's doctrine." The Cardinal
was interested in examining what he called 'modernity's
doubts' about some of its cherished notions of science.
But he was quick to add that "it would be absurd on the
basis of these [Feyerabend's and others'] assertions to
construct a hurried apologetics. The faith does not grow
from resentment and the rejection of rationality, but from
its fundamental affirmation and from [faith's] being
inscribed in a still greater form of reason." But, as the
reaction to the Pope's scheduled appearance at La
Sapienza reveals, Ratzinger's 1990 analysis that the old
myth of the Galileo Affair had lost some of its appeal was
not entirely accurate.

'Lay Science'

The signatories of the 2008 letter of protest noted that
they were 'humiliated and offended' by what the Pope
had said more than seventeen years before. In their
commitment to what they called 'lay science' [*laicità
della scienza*], as distinct, no doubt, from science
seemingly contaminated by religion, we see the old battle
between lay and clerical cultures. If we needed any
further evidence, the events in Rome in January 2008

show us that the legend of the encounter between Galileo and the Inquisition continues to resonate in our day. These events also reveal the wider context in which the legend survives.

We can see that wider context in the first salvo against Pope Benedict's projected appearance at La Sapienza, in November 2007, when Professor emeritus Marcello Cini complained, in a letter to the Rector of the University, that it was dangerous to have the Pope at the university. Theology, he argued, had no place in a modern, public university. The Pope's strategy, according to Cini, has been cunning; ever since he was the 'head of the Holy Office', he has tried to use the rationality of the Enlightenment *philosophes* as a 'Trojan horse' to enter the citadel of science and to keep it under control of 'the pseudo-rationality of the dogmas of religion'. An example Cini cited in this regard is what he called the Pope's support for 'Intelligent Design', which, as he said, rejects Darwinian science. For Cini, nothing less than the cultural advances of the last several hundred years were at risk if the Pope were to speak at La Sapienza. We shall have occasion at the end of this account to return to the powerful legend, or rather legends, of Galileo's encounter with the Inquisition. It is important to recognise that so much of our understanding of that encounter is filtered through the lenses of these legends which are at the heart of what the modern world understands to be characteristically modern. What follows is not so much a detailed chronology of this encounter, but an analysis of some of the highlights in order to begin to acquire a better understanding of the Galileo Affair and to recognise the legends for what they are.

From Myth to History

New Heavens

Galileo Galilei was born in Pisa in 1564: the same year in which Michelangelo died and Shakespeare was born. It was twenty-one years after the publication of Copernicus' treatise on heliocentric astronomy; and forty-seven years after the appearance of Luther's ninety-five theses and the beginning of the Reformation. In fact, the Protestant Reformation, the Catholic response - especially the Council of Trent, whose final session ended in 1563 - the destruction of the religious unity of Europe, and the ensuing wars of religion constitute the world in which Galileo will spend his entire life.

After studying at the University of Pisa and then teaching from 1592 at the University of Padua, Galileo became fascinated with the newly developed telescope, which he perfected in Padua in 1609. Galileo's telescopic observations convinced him that Copernicus was correct to claim that the Earth revolved around the Sun. In *The Starry Messenger*, published in 1610, he reported his discoveries that the Milky Way consists of innumerable stars, that the Moon has mountains, and that Jupiter has four satellites. Subsequently, he discovered the phases of Venus and spots on the surface of the Sun. He named the moons of Jupiter the 'Medicean Stars' and was rewarded by Cosimo de' Medici, Grand Duke of Tuscany, with appointment as chief mathematician and philosopher at the Duke's court in Florence. The telescopic discoveries, and arguments derived from them, served Galileo well in his public defense of Copernicus' thesis that the Earth and the other planets revolve about the Sun.

Galileo did not think, however, that his telescopic discoveries provided a *proof* for the view that the Earth rotated on its axis and revolved about the Sun. He did think that they provided arguments for the plausibility of Copernican astronomy, and he knew the difference between providing plausible arguments for a position and demonstrating that it is true. His discovery of the phases of Venus required only that Venus must revolve about the Sun. Even the discovery of spots on the Sun, and the fact that these spots moved across the Sun's surface, only provided evidence that the Sun was not an incorruptible body, as traditional cosmology claimed. None of Galileo's telescopic discoveries required the abandonment of a modified geocentric system (one with the Earth at the centre) - much less did they affirm the truth of a heliocentric one (one with the Sun at the centre). Indeed, the astronomical system proposed by

Tycho Brahe (1546-1601), according to which the various planets revolved about the Sun, which in turn revolved about a stationary Earth, remained at least a theoretical possibility.

In *The Starry Messenger*, Galileo claimed that his most important discovery were the four moons of Jupiter. This discovery, according to Galileo, provided

> ...an excellent and splendid argument for taking away the scruples of those who, while tolerating with equanimity the revolution of the planets around the Sun in the Copernican system, are so disturbed by the attendance of one Moon around the Earth while the two together complete the annual orb around the Sun, that they conclude that this constitution of the universe must be overthrown as impossible. For here we have not only one planet revolving around another while both run through a great circle around the Sun: but our vision offers us four stars wandering around Jupiter like the Moon around the Earth while all together with Jupiter traverse a great circle around the Sun in the space of twelve years.

Copernican astronomy required two centres of heavenly motion: the Moon's revolving around the Earth, and the Earth's and the other planets' revolving around the Sun. Such a universe, with more than one centre of motion, seemed inconceivable. Since it was now clear that four moons revolved around Jupiter, and Jupiter itself moved around another centre, an important objection to Copernican astronomy disappears.

Arguments Versus Proof

When we speak of Galileo's defense of the thesis that the Earth moves, we must be especially careful to distinguish between arguments in favour of a position and arguments which prove a position to be true. In fact, Galileo and the theologians of the Inquisition accepted the prevailing Aristotelian ideal of scientific demonstration which required that science be sure and certain knowledge in terms of necessary causes, not the conclusions of hypothetical or probabilistic reasoning which today we tend to accept as science. Galileo, despite his disagreements with many 17th Century Aristotelians, never departed from Aristotle's ideal of science as sure, certain knowledge. Whether he was arguing about the movement of the Earth or about laws that govern the motion of falling bodies, his goal was to achieve true, scientific demonstrations.

When Galileo wrote his *Two New Sciences*, near the end of his life, he argued that he deserved credit for establishing *new* sciences because his arguments employ 'necessary demonstrations' which proceed from 'unquestionable foundations'. It is especially important to recognise, as I have already indicated, that Galileo himself did not think that his astronomical observations provided sufficient evidence to prove that the Earth moves, although he did think that they called into question the truth of Ptolemaic astronomy (the geocentric system named after the 2nd Century Greek astronomer Ptolemy). Galileo hoped eventually to argue conclusively from the fact of ocean tides to the double motion of the Earth as the only possible cause, but he did not succeed.

Galileo's telescopic observations, described in *The Starry Messenger* and the *Letters on Sunspots*, provided the occasion for a renewed consideration of Copernican astronomy. At the very least, certain conclusions of traditional geocentric astronomy could no longer be maintained. Christopher Clavius, the famous Jesuit mathematician at the Collegio Romano, had written as early as 1611 that as a result of what Galileo had discovered and what he himself had seen through the telescope, astronomers will now have "to consider how the celestial orbs may be arranged in order to save these phenomena." Since the astronomical system of Tycho Brahe remained a possibility, the rejection of Ptolemy did not require the acceptance of Copernicus.

The public position which Galileo occupied in Florence from 1610 involved him in controversy. As the best-known advocate for Copernican astronomy, he was a lightning rod for criticism. Philosophers, for example, were concerned with the apparent violation of the principles of Aristotelian physics involved in the notion that the Earth moved and the Sun stood still, or that celestial bodies were in any way like the Earth. Criticism also came from some theologians who were troubled about the relationship between Copernican astronomy and the Bible. The story in the Book of Joshua concerning the Sun's standing still to allow the Israelites to win a battle seemed clearly to indicate that, normally, the Sun moves. Passages from the Psalms about the Earth's being fixed in its foundations seemed to affirm its immobility.

Cardinal Bellarmino and Copernican Astronomy

Galileo visited Rome on several occasions in the second decade of the 17th Century; he discussed his telescopic observations with Jesuit professors at the Collegio Romano and with members of the Church hierarchy, and early on he was very warmly received. In early 1615, well after the debate had begun, a Carmelite priest in Naples, Paolo Foscarini (1580-1616), published an essay in which he claimed that the Bible could be interpreted in such a way as to be consistent with Copernican astronomy.

Foscarini, calling upon exegetical principles well-known to Catholic theologians such as Melchior Cano (1509-1560), observed that "when Sacred Scripture attributes something to God or to any creature which would be improper and incommensurate, then it should be interpreted and explained...either metaphorically...or according to our mode of consideration, apprehension, conception, understanding, [and] knowing...[as] the Holy Spirit frequently and deliberately adopts the vulgar [i.e., popular] and common way of speaking". A classic example of this mode of attribution in Scripture are statements about God's stretching out his hand, walking in a garden, or showing emotions. All such statements must be taken metaphorically or as accommodating our limited mode of understanding God. If it were true that the Earth moves - a claim about one of God's creatures - "it would be easy," Foscarini writes, "to reconcile it with those passages of Sacred Scripture which are contrary to it...by saying that in those places Scripture speaks according to our mode of understanding, and according to appearances, and in respect to us. For thus it is that these bodies appear to be related to us and are described by the common and vulgar mode of thinking; namely, the Earth seems to stand still and to be immobile, and the Sun seems to revolve around it." Foscarini concludes that "in matters which pertain to the natural sciences and which are discovered and are open to investigation by human reason, Sacred Scripture ought not to be interpreted otherwise than according to what human reason itself establishes from natural experience and according to what is clear from innumerable data. ... [If the heliocentric system is true] we ought not to affirm emphatically that the sacred writings favour the Ptolemaic or the Aristotelian opinion, and thus create a crisis for the inviolable and most august sacred writings themselves. Rather we ought to interpret those writings in such a way as to make clear to all that their truth is in no way contrary to the arguments and experiences of the human sciences."

Foscarini sent his essay to Cardinal Roberto Bellarmino (known in English as Robert Bellarmine) (1542-1621), the learned Jesuit and member of the Inquisition in Rome. Bellarmino, already an old man, had spent his professional career refuting the views of Protestant theologians. Late in the 16th Century he had been named Professor of Controversial Theology at the new Jesuit university in Rome, and he was skilled in the intricacies of biblical interpretation as well as in challenges to the authority of the Church.

'Saving the Appearances'

Cardinal Bellarmino's response to Foscarini, a copy of which was sent to Galileo, is one of the most important documents for our analysis. In April 1615, the Cardinal writes:

> First...it appears to me that you [Foscarini] and Signore Galileo are proceeding prudently by limiting yourselves to speaking hypothetically and not absolutely [*ex suppositione e non assolutamente*], as I have always believed Copernicus did. For to say that, by assuming the Earth moves and the Sun stands still, one saves all the appearances better than by postulating eccentrics and epicycles is to speak well. This has no danger in it, and it suffices for mathematicians. But to wish to affirm that the Sun is really fixed in the centre of the heavens and merely turns upon itself without traveling from east to west, and that the Earth...revolves very swiftly around the Sun, is a very dangerous thing, likely not only to irritate all the scholastic theologians and philosophers, but also to harm our Holy Faith by rendering Holy Scripture false...

Notice the distinction Cardinal Bellarmino draws between speaking 'hypothetically' and speaking 'absolutely'. To speak hypothetically, in the sense the Cardinal means, is 'to save the appearances', and in astronomy 'to save the appearances' is to provide a consistent mathematical description of the observed phenomena. Hence, Bellarmino refers to the eccentrics and epicycles of Ptolemaic astronomy, which are mathematical constructs to describe observed movements in the heavens. To speak 'absolutely' would be to specify what the movements in the heavens really are. This is a standard distinction employed by medieval scientists and philosophers. Mathematical astronomy, which 'saved the appearances,' must be distinguished from what we might call physical astronomy, which has as its goal a true account of the nature of the heavens. Thomas Aquinas, for example, observes that Ptolemaic astronomy provides only a model for the observed phenomena and that one could very well have a mathematical model in which the Earth moves.

Bellarmino is wrong in thinking that Copernicus was only interested in saving the phenomena. In an unsigned foreword to Copernicus' 1543 text, Andreas Osiander, in order to protect Copernicus from criticism, wrote that the arguments were only hypothetical. Upon reading the text itself, however, one could see that Copernicus thought his astronomical system was true. Most scholars were aware of Copernicus' real position, and it may be that Bellarmino was only offering pastoral advice to Galileo and Foscarini, suggesting to them a prudential way to advance their arguments.

Contradicting Scripture

Cardinal Bellarmino next raises a theological objection:

> Second. I say that, as you know, the Council [of
> Trent] would prohibit expounding the Scriptures
> contrary to the common agreement of the Holy
> Fathers; and if Your Reverence [Foscarini] would
> read not only all their works but the commentaries
> of modern writers on Genesis, Psalms, Ecclesiastes,
> and Joshua, you would find that all agree in
> expounding literally that the Sun is in the heavens
> and travels swiftly around the Earth, while the Earth
> is far from the heavens and remains motionless in
> the center of the world. Now consider, with your
> sense of prudence, whether the Church could
> support giving Scripture a meaning contrary to the
> Holy Fathers and to all the Greek and Latin
> expositors. Nor may one reply that this is a not a
> matter of faith, because if it is not a matter of faith
> with regard to the subject matter [*ex parte obiecti*],
> it is with regard to the one who has spoken [*ex parte
> dicentis*]. Thus that man would be just as much a
> heretic who denied that Abraham had two sons and
> Jacob twelve, as one who denied the virgin birth of
> Christ, for both are declared by the Holy Ghost
> through the mouths of the prophets and apostles.

The Cardinal's reference to the decree of the fourth session (1546) of the Council of Trent has a special relevance. In addition to making clear what books constituted the canon of Scripture, the Council decreed that with respect to "matters of faith and morals" no one is permitted to interpret the Bible contrary to "that sense which Holy Mother Church, to whom it belongs to judge their true sense and meaning, has held and does hold". Nor may one interpret Scripture contrary to the "unanimous agreement" of the Church Fathers. In invoking the authority of the Council, Bellarmino extends the sense of "faith and morals" to include historical and scientific claims found in the Bible, since to deny the truth of what the Bible says on any matter appears to call into question the affirmation that the entire Bible is God's revealed word.

Despite the Cardinal's claim that the Church's understanding of the Bible was involved in the dispute, he is willing to examine the arguments of the new astronomy.

> Third...if there were a true demonstration that the Sun is in the centre of the universe...and that the Sun does not circle the Earth but the Earth circles the Sun, then one would have to proceed with great care in explaining the Scriptures that appear contrary, and say rather that we do not understand

them than that what is demonstrated is false. But I will not believe that there is such a demonstration until it is shown to me. Nor is it the same to demonstrate that by supposing the Sun to be at the centre and the Earth in heaven one can save the appearances, and to demonstrate that in truth the Sun is at the centre and the Earth in heaven; for I believe the first demonstration may be available, but I have very grave doubts about the second, and in the case of doubt one must not abandon the Holy Scripture as interpreted by the Holy Fathers...

Proof and the Status Quo

This final paragraph in Bellarmino's response to Foscarini is very important. Note, that he again draws a distinction between saving the appearances and demonstrating the truth of a position. Note further that, despite his very grave doubts, he admits the possibility of a demonstration for the motion of the Earth, although he is aware of no such demonstration. In the absence of such a demonstration, prudence, at least, requires that the traditional interpretation of those passages of the Bible which claim that the Earth is motionless be maintained. It is clear from the Cardinal's comments that he did not think that the immobility of the Earth was a matter of

Church doctrine. If Bellarmino had thought it were conclusively a matter of faith, he could not argue, as he did, that it might be possible to demonstrate that the Earth does move. For then he would have argued that scientific truth could contradict the truth of faith.

The opposition within scientific circles in the early 17th Century to claims that the Earth moved was generally based on the assumption that a geocentric astronomy was an essential part of a larger Aristotelian cosmology: the view, that is, that Aristotelian physics and metaphysics depended in some way on the affirmation that the Earth was immobile at the centre of the universe. Thus, if one were to reject such a geocentric astronomy, then, *so it seemed to many*, the whole of Aristotelian science would have to be discarded. As a result of such an understanding, or really, misunderstanding, of the interdependence of astronomy, cosmology, physics, and metaphysics, some thought that the acceptance of a moving Earth would involve a radical philosophical revolution. Hence, we might understand why many of Galileo's contemporaries were so troubled by his support for Copernican astronomy. Furthermore, although we now accept without question that the Earth moves, we need to guard against assuming that it is a simple matter to reach this conclusion and that, therefore, the scientific opponents of Galileo were either simple-minded or stubbornly blind to the truth.

The Aristotelian Ideal

An understanding of the theological dimensions of the encounter between Galileo and the Inquisition requires that we keep in mind this question concerning the scientific knowledge of the motion of the Earth. All sides in the controversy were committed to the Aristotelian ideal of scientific knowledge. Remember, Cardinal Bellarmino told Foscarini and Galileo that if there were a demonstration for the motion of the Earth, then the Bible would have to be interpreted accordingly. The Cardinal has simply reaffirmed traditional Catholic teaching that the truths of science and the truths of faith cannot contradict one another.

We know that, by 1615, Galileo was convinced that he was on the verge of achieving a demonstration for the motion of the Earth, but he needed time. He sought to prevent the Church from condemning as heretical the claim that the Earth moves, when he was about to demonstrate that in fact the Earth does move. Galileo expected that an argument from the phenomenon of the ocean tides would provide the necessary demonstration. He circulated a manuscript on this subject in late 1615 and early 1616, and the argument appears in the final section of his *Dialogue Concerning the Two Chief World Systems*, published in 1632.

So, in 1615 and 1616 neither Galileo nor the Inquisition thought there was a demonstration for the motion of the Earth: Galileo expected, indeed anticipated, such a demonstration; the Inquisition did not. In the absence of a demonstration, Cardinal Bellarmino had urged prudence: do not challenge the traditionally accepted readings of those biblical passages which have been interpreted as affirming the immobility of the Earth. The Cardinal was acutely aware of Protestant challenges to the Catholic Church's claim to be the sole, legitimate interpreter of God's word. In many ways we see the Inquisition especially concerned with maintaining the authority of the Church against all who seemed to threaten it. Bellarmino, veteran of theological controversies with Protestants, was always alert to point out that the principal theological issue of the day with respect to the Bible was not so much what Scripture meant as who had the authority authentically to interpret it. The Cardinal did recognise the difficulties in discovering truths in Scripture. For him, every sentence in the Bible has a literal or historical meaning, i.e., "the meaning which the words immediately present." Yet, the literal meaning is either *simple*, "which consists of the proper meaning of the words", or *figurative*, "in which words are transferred from their natural signification to another." When the Bible refers to "the right hand of God", for example, the simple literal sense would mean a part of God's body; whereas the figurative literal sense, and the one which should be adopted, means God's power. Bellarmino argued that serious exegetical errors can arise "either by reading figuratively what should be taken as simply literal or by reading as simply literal what should be taken as figurative." The Cardinal, in distinguishing between the simple literal sense and the figurative literal sense, often wrote that one must distinguish between *res quae dicuntur* (what is said) and *modus quo dicuntur* (the way it is said). In the controversy concerning Copernican astronomy and the Bible, it seems however that the Cardinal's priority was the protection of the Church's authority as the authentic interpreter of Scripture and not the specific question of whether the motion of the Sun and the stability of the Earth should be taken as simply literal or figurative. Perhaps this commitment helps to explain his expansive interpretation of the Council of Trent's injunction prohibiting dissent from the traditional understanding of the Bible with respect to matters of "faith and morals." The debates of the Reformation offer an important context for understanding Bellarmino's and, ultimately, the Inquisition's position.

Galileo on Science and Scripture

During the momentous years of 1615 and 1616, as the discussion about the relationship between the new astronomy and the Bible reached into the highest circles of the Catholic Church, Galileo was increasingly concerned that the authorities in the Church might act foolishly and conclude that there was an incompatibility between heliocentric astronomy and the Bible.

We can see the general outline of Galileo's position in the note he wrote to himself as he sketched his response to Bellarmino's letter to Foscarini:

> The motion of the Earth and the stability of the Sun could never be against Faith or Holy Scripture, if this proposition were correctly proved to be physically true by philosophers, astronomers, and mathematicians, with the help of sense experience, accurate observations, and necessary demonstrations. However, in this case, if some passages of Scripture were to sound contrary, we would have to say that this is due to the weakness of our mind, which is unable to grasp the true meaning of Scripture in this particular case. This is the common doctrine, and it is entirely right, since one truth cannot contradict another truth. On the other hand, whoever wants to condemn it judicially must first demonstrate it to be

physically false by collecting the reasons against it...
If the Earth de facto moves, we cannot change nature
and arrange for it not to move. But we can rather
easily remove the opposition of Scripture with the
mere admission that we do not grasp its true
meaning. Therefore the way to be sure not to err is to
begin with astronomical and physical investigations,
and not with scriptural ones.

Letter to the Grand Duchess

Galileo addresses the question of the relationship between
science and the Bible in his most extensive and systematic
way in his famous *Letter to the Grand Duchess Christina*.
Galileo is the chief scientist in the employ of the Medici
family and Christina of Lorraine is the mother of the
reigning Grand Duke. The letter contains Galileo's
account of the recent controversy over the claims of
Copernican astronomy. He composes it in 1615, after
having read Bellarmino's response to Foscarini, and, as I
mentioned, in the midst of the debate concerning the
relationship between traditional interpretations of the
Bible and the view that the Earth moves.

By addressing the letter to the Grand Duchess, rather
than to theologians in Rome, Galileo is able to write to an
educated lay audience, even though his primary audience

are the authorities of the Inquisition in Rome. Galileo is
not a theologian, and theologians in Rome might well
dismiss a theological treatise directly addressed to them
by Galileo the mathematician and physicist.

Rhetoric Versus Proof

Galileo is well-trained in Renaissance techniques of
rhetoric and a failure to recognise Galileo's skills in this
respect has resulted in uncritical readings of the letter. For
example, many modern history texts accept without
question Galileo's own account of the history of the
controversy, which he presents in the first few paragraphs
of the letter. We must remember when we read his
account that, first of all it is his interpretation of the
events, and, second, that he has chosen his facts carefully
in order to achieve his end: *to persuade* the authorities of
the Catholic Church not to act foolishly and condemn
Copernican astronomy.

He identifies his enemies as being unable to refute him
in science, and as a result, they "try to shield the fallacies
of their arguments with the cloak of simulated
religiousness and with the authority of Holy Scripture,
unintelligently using the latter [the Bible] for the
confutation of arguments they neither understand nor
have heard." The story he tells of Copernicus is
interesting. He misidentifies him as a priest, argues that

his investigations were undertaken at the request of the Pope, and, noting that Copernicus' book was dedicated to the Pope, Galileo claims: "Once printed, this book was accepted by the Holy Church, and it was read and studied all over the world without anyone's ever having the least scruple about its doctrine." Galileo concludes his historical observations with the following remark:

> Finally, now that one is discovering how well founded upon clear observations and necessary demonstrations this doctrine is, some persons come along who, without having seen the book, give its author the reward of so much work by trying to have him declared a heretic; this they do only in order to satisfy their special animosity, groundlessly conceived against someone else [Galileo, himself] who has no greater connection with Copernicus than the endorsement of his doctrine.

Note what Galileo claims and what he does not claim. His comments, at first glance, suggest that Copernican astronomy has been demonstrated to be true, or perhaps has been shown to be true on the basis of 'clear observations,' no doubt Galileo's telescopic discoveries. But on closer inspection, we see that all Galileo is claiming is that Copernican astronomy is "well founded upon clear observations and necessary demonstrations."

To show that a position is 'well founded' is not
necessarily to show that it has been demonstrated to be
true. Galileo is aware of the importance of necessary
demonstrations; he has in mind Bellarmino's distinctions
in the Cardinal's letter to Foscarini. In fact, throughout
the *Letter to the Grand Duchess*, Galileo uses the phrase
"necessary demonstrations" frequently, without once
offering such a demonstration for the motion of the Earth.
Remember the rhetorical nature of the letter; Galileo
seeks to persuade the officers of the Inquisition not to
condemn Copernican astronomy. Galileo knows that
theologians in Rome accept, at least in principle, the
position that the truths of science and the truths of faith
cannot contradict one another, and that, if there is a
scientific demonstration on a particular subject, it would
not be possible for the Bible to be authentically
interpreted in a way which contradicts what science
demonstrates. As he said, this is "the common doctrine."
Remember, in addition, that both Galileo and the officers
of the Inquisition share the same Aristotelian ideal of
scientific knowledge; both sides understand what a
demonstration is. If Galileo, in fact, had a demonstration
for the motion of the Earth, he surely would have
presented it, for he knew that a demonstration would
prevent the Church's condemnation of Copernican
astronomy. We see here another reason for ostensibly

addressing the letter to the Grand Duchess, for she would not be expected to follow a complex scientific demonstration; it would be sufficient for her chief scientist simply to suggest that one existed.

God the Author of Scripture and Nature

Throughout the *Letter to the Grand Duchess*, Galileo reaffirms traditional Catholic teaching on the relationship between science and scripture. God is the author of both the book of nature and the book of scripture. Therefore, the truths of nature and scripture cannot contradict one another. Accordingly, Galileo writes:

> I think that in disputes about natural phenomena one must begin not with the authority of scriptural passages, but with sensory experiences and necessary demonstrations. For the Holy Scripture and nature derive equally from the Godhead, the former as the dictation of the Holy Spirit and the latter as the obedient executrix of God's orders; moreover, to accommodate the understanding of the common people it is appropriate for Scripture to say many things that are different in appearance and in regard to the surface meaning of the words from the absolute truth ... and so it seems that natural phenomena which are placed before our

eyes by sensory experience or proved by necessary demonstrations should not be called into question, let alone condemned, on account of scriptural passages whose words appear to have a different meaning.

One must know how to discover the true meaning of Scripture since this does not always correspond to the surface meaning of the words. Furthermore, we must remember, as Cardinal Cesare Baronius (1538-1607) famously noted, that the primary purpose of the Bible is not to reveal how the heavens go, but how to go to heaven. In his attempt to persuade the Inquisition not to condemn Copernican astronomy, Galileo asks rhetorically: "can an opinion be both heretical and irrelevant to the salvation of souls?" Cardinal Bellarmino might well respond that there are different senses of 'irrelevant.' It may well be that, from the point of view of the subject matter, an astronomical claim is irrelevant to salvation, but if this topic is discussed in the Bible then the question is relevant to salvation in that it is a matter of faith that the Bible is true from beginning to end. We have seen, however, that Cardinal Bellarmino understands that the true meaning of the Bible may be difficult to discern in a particular instance; the Cardinal is well aware that the true meaning of the text may be expressed in metaphors and similes.

Galileo does recognise the authority of the Church to determine the true meaning of the Bible, but he urges those in Rome to beware of mischievous advice from his opponents and that the Church should not "flash the sword [simply because she] has the power to do it, without considering that it is not always right to do all that one can do." Galileo argues that it is contrary to Catholic practice "to use scriptural passages to establish conclusions about nature, when by means of observation and necessary demonstrations one could at some point demonstrate the contrary of what the surface meaning of the words affirm."

Galileo and Catholic Orthodoxy

Galileo quotes famous Catholic theologians, most notably, St Augustine, and he leaves these quotations in the authoritative, original Latin. He finds support for the continuity of his views with Catholic orthodoxy in passages from Augustine's *On the Literal Meaning of Genesis* such as this one: "In obscure subjects very far removed from our eyes, it may happen that even in the divine writings we read things that can be interpreted in different ways by different people, all consistent with the faith we have; in such a case, let us not rush into any one of these interpretations with such precipitous commitment that we are ruined if it is

rightly undermined by a more diligent and truth-
ful investigation."

Another passage from Augustine serves Galileo's
purposes well: "There should be no doubt about the
following: whenever experts of this world can truly
demonstrate something about natural phenomena, we
should show it not to be contrary to our Scripture; but
whenever in their books they teach something contrary
to the Holy Writ, we should without any doubt hold it to
be most false and also show this by any means we
can..." After citing this text from Augustine, Galileo
employs a particularly deft argument: the words of St
Augustine imply:

> ...the following doctrine: in the learned books of
> worldly authors are contained some propositions
> about nature which are truly demonstrated and
> others which are simply taught; in regard to the
> former [those truly demonstrated], the task of
> wise theologians is to show that they are not
> contrary to Holy Scripture; as for the latter
> (which are taught but not demonstrated with
> necessity), if they contain anything contrary to
> the Holy Writ, then they should be considered
> indubitably false and must be demonstrated such
> by every possible means.

In which of these two categories would one put the argument for the motion of the Earth in 1615? Galileo is so certain that he is about to have a demonstration for the motion of the Earth that he grants to the Bible an authority on scientific matters that both Augustine and Aquinas would deny. Perhaps he thought that such obeisance to biblical authority on his part might ingratiate him to the Inquisition in Rome. In fact, in a rather clever move, Galileo seems to turn the tables on the Inquisition: "therefore, before condemning a physical proposition, one must show that it is not conclusively demonstrated. Furthermore, it is much more reasonable and natural that this be done not by those who hold it to be true, but by those who regard it to be false..."

You might imagine how a theologian in Rome would evaluate Galileo's argument. Despite all the rhetoric of necessary demonstrations, one searches the letter in vain to find one. Rather than provide a scientific demonstration, Galileo expects theologians to enter the arena of science to show that a particular proposition is not 'conclusively demonstrated.'

The Inquisition Acts: 1616

In many ways, Galileo's principles were shared by his opponents in the Inquisition, although they reached a different conclusion when they examined the particular case of Copernican astronomy. In early 1616 the cardinals of the Inquisition instructed their theological consultants formally to consider the status of the new astronomy in the light of biblical revelation. The consultants issued their report in February 1616, which concluded that the claim that the Sun was immobile and at the centre of the universe was:

> ...foolish and absurd in philosophy, and formally heretical since it explicitly contradicts in many places the sense of Holy Scripture, according to the literal meaning of the words and according to the common interpretation and understanding of the Holy Fathers and the doctors of theology.

The theologians also concluded that the claim that the Earth moves was also foolish and absurd in philosophy and, "in regard to theological truth it is at least erroneous in faith." Although we have the text of the report, we need to remember that it is just that, a committee report of consultants and not a formal Church pronouncement.

It is important to note that the first part of each of these two conclusions reached by the theologians is that Copernican astronomy is 'false and absurd' philosophically, that is, scientifically. Why should the theological experts of the Inquisition care whether Copernican astronomy is false scientifically? The theologians were committed to the complementarity between science and scripture. If a proposed scientific proposition is false, scripture cannot be in agreement with it, since the Bible cannot affirm as true that which reason knows to be false. Furthermore, in reaching the conclusion that Copernican astronomy contradicts the Bible, the theologians accepted as incontrovertibly true a particular geocentric cosmology, and, on the basis of such an acceptance, they insisted that the Bible be read in a certain way. Thus, in part, they subordinated scriptural interpretation to a physical theory. They proceeded in this manner because, like Galileo, they were convinced that the Bible contained scientific truths and that, on the basis of what is known to be true in the natural sciences, one could discover the same truth in related biblical passages. They do not argue - as most commentators mistakenly think - that the proposition is false scientifically *because* it contradicts the Bible. In fact, their argument is just the opposite. Furthermore, just as some philosophers mistakenly concluded that Aristotelian physics and metaphysics depended on a geocentric cosmology, so some theologians feared that, a rejection of Aristotle's view that the Earth does not move, would call into question all of Aristotelian philosophy, a philosophy upon which important elements of Catholic theology depended.

The Inquisition Report

After the consulting theologians issued their report to the cardinals of the Inquisition, Cardinal Bellarmino, on instructions from Pope Paul V, ordered Galileo not to hold, teach, or defend the condemned propositions. Books, like Foscarini's, which argued for the compatibility between the new astronomy and the Bible were prohibited, and the publication of Copernicus' book was to be suspended until corrections could be made to it. The corrections eventually ordered by the Congregation of the Index of Forbidden Books involved changing those passages in which Copernicus claims that in fact the Earth moves to read that he simply supposes or hypothesises that the Earth moves. The distinction between speaking hypothetically and speaking absolutely, which Bellarmino had urged upon Galileo in April 1615, as prudential advice, now served as the basis for the disciplinary decrees of the Inquisition and the Index of Forbidden Books.

One week after learning of the 1616 decision of the Inquisition, Galileo wrote to the Secretary of State to the Grand Duke of Tuscany to inform him what had transpired. Galileo had been in Rome since December 1615, hoping to use his influence to prevent the condemnation of Copernican astronomy. He was acutely aware that some Florentine theologians had accused him of affirming a position that was "heretical and against the faith." Galileo observed that his opponents "tried orally and in writing to make this idea prevail, but events have shown that [this]...effort did not find approval with the Holy Church. She [the Church] has only decided that the opinion does not agree with Holy Scripture, and thus only those books are prohibited which have explicitly maintained that it does not conflict with Scripture." Indeed, the public decree of the Index of Forbidden Books of March 1616 gave as a reason for the prohibition of certain texts that the new astronomy was "contrary to Holy Scripture." The phrase "formally heretical", used by the theological consultants to the Inquisition, was omitted in the public document. Although Galileo did not mention in this letter the specific injunction communicated to him, it seems that he did not view what transpired to be so serious as it has since been interpreted. In May 1616 Galileo obtained a formal statement from Cardinal Bellarmino concerning what had happened when the Cardinal had informed Galileo of the Inquisition's orders to him in March of that year. According to Bellarmino, Galileo had not been required to recant any views he held; "he [Galileo] has only been notified of the declaration made by the Holy Father [Pope Paul V] and published by the Sacred Congregation of the Index, whose content is that the doctrine attributed to

Copernicus (that the Earth moves around the Sun and the Sun stands at the centre of the world without moving from east to west) is contrary to Holy Scripture and therefore cannot be defended or held."

Knowledge Versus Conviction

What is clear in the actions of 1616 is that the theologians of the Inquisition thought that the Bible contained scientific truths. Since it was obvious, from science, that the Earth does not move, and since certain passages in the Bible seemed clearly to say or to imply the same thing, it must be the case that the Bible proclaims that the Earth does not move. Furthermore, in the face of the Protestant Reformation, the Catholic Church was particularly alert to threats, real or imagined, to traditional interpretations of the Bible and to the authority of the Church to determine the true meaning of the Bible. In ordering Galileo not to hold or teach Copernican astronomy, the Inquisition did not think that it was requiring Galileo to choose between faith and science. Nor, in the absence of scientific knowledge for the motion of the Earth, would Galileo have thought that he was asked to make such a choice. Here it is important to remember that Galileo and the Inquisition thought that science was absolutely certain knowledge, guaranteed by rigorous demonstrations.

Being *convinced* that the Earth moves is different from *knowing* that it moves.

The *disciplinary* decree of the Inquisition, that is, the private injunction given to Galileo, was unwise and imprudent: but, as I have already indicated, the Inquisition's actions were based on the subordination of the interpretation of certain passages of the Bible to a geocentric cosmology, a cosmology which would eventually be rejected. Such an action is just the opposite of the domination of science by religious faith! Surely the conclusion of the theological consultants is an example of the failure to distinguish between a question of science and the proper interpretation of Scripture, and the failure resulted in disciplinary errors. The only public statement made by the Church in 1616 was the official act of the Index of Forbidden Books, itself an exclusively disciplinary agency. The famous trial of Galileo in 1633, after the publication of his *Dialogue Concerning the Two Chief World System*, depends on the decisions reached seventeen years earlier. The theological, philosophical, and scientific questions which constitute the heart of the controversy are clear by 1616. The Inquisition expected Galileo to obey its orders not to hold, teach, or defend Copernican astronomy. As we shall see, the cardinals who sat in judgment of Galileo in 1633 were convinced that he had violated that injunction and they then demanded that he formally and publicly renounce the views proscribed seventeen years before.

Preparations for the *Dialogue Concerning the Two Chief World Systems* (1632) and the Trial of Galileo (1633)

Galileo had been committed to publishing the *Dialogue* for some time. Already in *The Starry Messenger* in 1610 he promised to provide a demonstration for the motion of the Earth in a future book on the 'system of the world.' During the second decade of the 17th Century, Galileo was occupied with replying to, criticising, and refuting his critics on a number of fronts: concerning his telescopic observations; in his debates with opponents in Tuscany concerning his views on floating bodies (1611-1615); in arguments with Christopher Scheiner over sunspots (1613); concerning theological objections to Copernican astronomy (1612-1616); and with Orazio Grassi on the nature of comets. Galileo also spent time working out details of his discoveries, such as calculating the periods of revolution of the moons of Jupiter.

I have already mentioned that in late 1615 he had circulated a treatise in which he argued that the phenomenon of the ocean tides might provide the kind of evidence which would lead necessarily to the conclusion of the double motion of the Earth as the cause. Just as water moves in a basin which is set in motion, so water on the surface of the Earth might move because the Earth moves. It is this argument which appears in the fourth day of the *Dialogue*. The 1616 injunction of the Inquisition did not prevent the private circulation of Galileo's treatise on the tides but it did mean that Galileo would have to adjust his plans to write a book on *the* system of the world which would have been simply an elaboration of his argument for Copernican astronomy on the basis of the tides.

Pope Urban VIII

In April 1624, the year after the election of Cardinal Maffeo Barberini as Pope Urban VIII, Galileo journeyed to Rome and had six long audiences with his old friend. Galileo had dedicated *The Assayer* to the newly elected Pope in 1623, and the Pope had listened approvingly as the book was read to him. Reports of their discussions indicate that the Pope told Galileo that there would be no problem in writing about Copernican astronomy so long as he restricted his presentation to the *hypothetical*. We have already encountered one sense of 'hypothetical' in the traditional view that mathematical astronomy simply 'saved the appearances'; it could not in principle arrive at the truths of heavenly motions. The distinction between 'hypothetical' and 'true,' and the confusion concerning different senses of 'hypothetical,' play an important role in Galileo's encounter with the Inquisition. In Bellarmino's letter to Foscarini (1615), which we have already discussed, the Cardinal drew a distinction between mathematical astronomers who speak hypothetically (*ex suppositione*) and 'save the appearances' by using epicycles, deferents, and the like, and physicists who have as their goal the discovery of the true structure of the cosmos. Bellarmino, following Thomas Aquinas, was well aware that Ptolemaic astronomy fell into the former category. Epicycles and eccentrics are geometric devices to describe observed celestial motions and as such were 'hypotheses.' Geometric entities could not serve as necessary, physical causes of the observed motions of the heavens. Bellarmino noted that, since such hypotheses could not, in principle, constitute a true science of the heavens, there was no danger of their being in conflict with biblical truths. As we have seen, Bellarmino did not deny that there can be scientific knowledge about the heavens; he did not think, however, that mathematical astronomy is such a science.

Hypotheses and Divine Omnipotence

There was considerable ambiguity in the use of the term 'hypothetical' in the early 17th Century. Thus, when different interlocutors use this term they do not always mean the same thing. In addition to the Thomistic tradition, in which Bellarmino participated, there was another one according to which the 'hypothetical' status of claims about nature reflected a scepticism about human intelligence: the tendency, that is, to view any claim about human knowledge as 'hypothetical.' In this tradition, to affirm divine omnipotence required, so it seemed, the denial of the possibility of human knowledge of the world. Since science, in the traditional Aristotelian sense, was knowledge of a necessary nexus between cause and effect, it seemed that to argue that this type of knowledge is possible was to necessitate God, and hence to deny divine omnipotence. Agostino Oregio (1577-1635), a colleague and friend of Maffeo Barberini (later Pope Urban VIII), reports a conversation Barberini had with Galileo sometime in 1615 or 1616. Barberini defended the view that, given God's omnipotence and omniscience, we ought not to "bind divine power and wisdom" by claiming that any human science knows for sure the way things are. Oregio was one of the theological consultants engaged by the Inquisition in 1632 to examine Galileo's *Dialogue*, and he was named a cardinal in November 1633. He also is a source for the conversations Pope Urban VIII had with Galileo in 1624, in which the Pope asked Galileo whether he agreed that unless you can show a particular claim about nature contains a contradiction then you have to admit that God has "the power and wisdom to arrange differently [from any theory Galileo advances] the orbs and the stars in such a way as to save the phenomena that appear in heaven." If God has the power and wisdom to arrange the heavens in a way different from any theory which we propose, while saving all the phenomena, "then we must not bind divine power and wisdom" by saying that a particular explanation of the heavens is true. The Pope confided to another of his cardinals that there ought to be no fear about Copernican astronomy since no one could possibly demonstrate it to be necessarily true. It seems that the Pope understood the 'hypothetical' character of Copernican astronomy to mean that it cannot possibly be true. This is a different understanding of 'hypothetical' from that which Aquinas used when he wrote of hypotheses in mathematical astronomy: as devices for saving the appearances they could not be *necessarily* true since they did not conform to the principles of a true science of nature. Aquinas, of course, accepted the view that a true science of nature was indeed possible.

The Dialogue

In the discussions surrounding the publication of the *Dialogue*, the Pope's chief theologian, Niccolo Riccardi, wrote to the inquisitors in Florence that the title of the book could not be *On the Ebb and Flow of the Tides* (as Galileo had originally planned), and that the opening and closing of the book had to reaffirm the hypothetical nature of the discussion. Riccardi's letter reveals the continuing importance for the Pope of maintaining the hypothetical character of the arguments concerning Copernican astronomy: the Pope thinks, Riccardi wrote, "that the title and subject should not focus on the ebb and flow but absolutely on the mathematical examination of the Copernican position on the Earth's motion, with the aim of proving that, if we remove divine revelation and sacred doctrine, the appearances could be saved with this supposition..." Galileo's negotiations with Riccardi in the early summer of 1630 resulted in the inclusion of an introduction, "to the discerning reader", in which Galileo claimed that he wrote the book to show that the 1616 prohibition of books that argued for the truth of the new astronomy was not the result of scientific ignorance in Catholic circles. His book would show that Catholic thinkers knew the arguments, but rejected them, and he would do this by taking "the Copernican point of view, proceeding in the manner of a pure mathematical hypothesis and striving in every contrived way to present it as superior to the viewpoint of the Earth's being motionless."

By writing the book in the form of a dialogue among a proponent of Copernicus (Salviati), a supporter of the

Ptolemaic and Aristotelian positions (Simplicio), and an intelligent, uncommitted third party (Sagredo), he thought that he would preserve the claim that he, the author, did not hold or teach Copernican astronomy. The arguments Galileo advanced for Copernican astronomy in the text did not claim to be a demonstration for the new astronomy, but nor did they take the form of mere fictive models to save the phenomena. In the first three parts (days) Galileo shows that none of the arguments advanced for the immobility of the Earth and the mobility of the Sun are conclusive; in fact, the defender of geostatic astronomy, Simplicio, does not fare well in the dialogue with Sagredo and Salviati. The demolition of arguments against the Earth's motion leads to the discussion in the fourth part of the positive argument for such motion based on the tides. Galileo does follow Riccardi's instructions to emphasise the suppositional character of the arguments in the final part of the book. It is, however, Simplicio, the defender of the discredited geostatic position who observes:

> I confess that your idea [concerning the tides] seems to me much more ingenious than any others I have heard, but I do not thereby regard it as true and conclusive. Indeed, I always keep before my mind's eye a very firm doctrine, which I once learned from

a man of great knowledge and eminence, and before which one must give pause. From it I know what you would answer if both of you [Sagredo and Salviati] are asked whether God with his infinite power and wisdom could give to the element of water the back and forth motion we see in it by some means other than by moving the containing basin; I say you will answer that he would have the power and the knowledge to do this in many ways, some of them even inconceivable by our intellect. Thus, I immediately conclude that in view of this it would be excessively bold if someone should want to limit and compel divine power and wisdom to a particular fancy of his.

Defending Copernicus

Galileo certainly thought that scientific knowledge of nature was possible; he did not accept the view that appeals to divine omnipotence rendered all human claims to knowledge 'hypothetical.' When authorities in Rome read the book they were convinced that Galileo had defended, *in some way*, Copernican astronomy. He had done precisely what he had been enjoined not to do in 1616.

In late summer of 1632 Pope Urban VIII ordered that publication of the book cease, and he appointed a special commission to examine it. Urban was especially insistent that the Inquisition act against Galileo. He may have felt personally betrayed in that Galileo's support for Copernican astronomy in the *Dialogue* was not 'hypothetical' in the sense which he had discussed with Galileo in 1624. Furthermore, the Pope's favourite argument concerning divine omnipotence and the impossibility of necessity in nature, needed for scientific demonstrations, was set forth by Simplicio, who often came out on the short end of discussions in the *Dialogue*. Also, in the midst of the Thirty Years War, the Pope had been experiencing increasing criticism of his foreign policy which 'tilted' toward the French and away from the Catholic cause championed by the Habsburgs. Insisting on treating Galileo firmly allowed the Pope to be seen as an ardent defender of orthodoxy and of the authority of the Church.

In September 1632 the papal commission concluded that Galileo "may have overstepped his instructions by asserting absolutely the Earth's motion and the Sun's immobility and thus deviating from hypothesis..." The commission noted that when Galileo brought his original manuscript to Rome in 1630 it was clear that although "he had been ordered to discuss the Copernican system only as a pure mathematical hypothesis, one found immediately that the book was not like this, but that it spoke absolutely, presenting the reasons for and against without deciding." Thus, Riccardi had insisted on a preface and an ending in which Galileo makes it explicit that he is only going to write hypothetically and that the entire text should conform to this approach. One of the conclusions the commission reached was that, despite the changes in the beginning and end of the book, Galileo had not really followed Riccardi's instructions. The commission was well-aware of the general prohibition of books defending Copernican astronomy which appeared in the Decree of the Index of Forbidden Books in March 1616, but it also discovered the 1616 document according to which the Inquisition specifically (albeit privately) instructed Galileo not to "hold, teach, or defend it [Copernican astronomy] in any way whatever, orally or in writing." The key phrase, "in any way whatever", plays an important role in the Inquisition's judgment of Galileo's guilt. This newly discovered document proved especially damning. As the Tuscan ambassador in Rome wrote to his superiors in Florence, this text alone was enough to ruin Galileo. Galileo was ordered to Rome for trial before the Inquisition in the late Spring of 1633.

One of the theologians asked to review the book for the Inquisition in 1633, Melchior Inchofer, concluded that throughout the book Galileo proceeded in a "categorical, absolute, and non-hypothetical manner." No doubt,

Inchofer was employing the term 'hypothetical' in that sense which opposes it to speaking 'absolutely'. As Inchofer observed: "Galileo promises [in the book] to proceed in the manner of a mathematical hypothesis, but a mathematical hypothesis is not established by physical and necessary conclusions... So Galileo should have posited the Earth's motion as something to be analysed deductively, not as something to be proved true by destroying the opposite view, as he indeed does in the entire work... So, in order to restrict himself to a pure mathematical hypothesis, Galileo did not have to prove absolutely that the Earth moves, but only to conceive its motion in the imagination without assuming it physically, and thereby explain celestial phenomena and derive the numerical details of the various motions."

The Sentence of the Inquisition

Thus, even though Galileo might say that he did not claim to demonstrate that the Earth moves, he still was not speaking 'hypothetically' in the sense that the authorities in Rome required. In the formal sentence of June 1633, the Inquisition noted that the Dialogue explicitly violated the 1616 injunction since Galileo, in this book, "defended the said opinion [of the Earth's motion and the Sun's stability] already condemned and so declared to your face, although in the said book you try by means of various subterfuges to give the impression of leaving it undecided and labeled as probable; this is still a very serious error since there is no way an opinion declared and defined contrary to divine Scripture may be probable." Note the argument that one cannot say that an opinion is probable if it has been declared and defined to be contrary to the Bible. It is important to remember the distinction between possible and probable. Probable means that the preponderance of evidence favors a view. Obviously, a Catholic must use the evidence of what Scripture says in determining whether a position is probable. To defend the opinion that the Earth moves and the Sun stands still as 'probable' would mean that one had ignored or seriously undervalued the clear evidence of the Bible, at least as the Inquisition thought such evidence existed. The certificate Galileo had from Cardinal Bellarmino (May 1616), which he presented at the Inquisition's proceedings in 1633, did not contain the injunction that he should not teach, hold, or defend, orally or in writing, in any manner whatsoever, Copernican astronomy. This certificate, however, did attest to the fact that Galileo had been told that this opinion was contrary to Scripture: a fact which only aggravated Galileo's case further in the eyes of his judges, since it showed that Galileo knew that the new astronomy was contrary to Scripture and yet he "dared to treat of it, defend it, and show it as probable."

After preliminary discussions before the Inquisition in April 1633, Galileo admitted that his book offered a stronger support for Copernican astronomy than he really intended, and that he regretted the error and would, if allowed, make changes in the book. A summary of the proceedings was sent to the Pope, who decided that Galileo must be interrogated to see what his intentions were in writing the book. This interrogation occurred on 21st June and Galileo denied any malicious intent. The cardinals of the Inquisition who sat in judgment of Galileo concluded that he was "vehemently suspected of heresy", a formal category less serious than being guilty of heresy, which would have included willful perseverance in a false doctrine.

In June 1633, the Inquisition, to ensure Galileo's obedience, required that he publicly and formally affirm that the Earth does not move. Galileo, however reluctantly, acquiesced. The Inquisition ordered that Galileo live under a kind of house arrest in his villa outside Florence, where he remained until his death in 1642. The meeting of the Inquisition, which decided Galileo's fate, was presided over by Pope Urban VIII and he formally approved the decision to make Galileo publicly recant his views. Nevertheless, from beginning to end, the actions of the Inquisition were disciplinary, not doctrinal, although they were often based on the erroneous notion that it was heretical to claim that the

Earth moves. Erroneous notions remain only notions; opinions of theologians are not the same as Christian doctrine. The error the Church made in dealing with Galileo was an error in judgment; the Inquisition was wrong to discipline Galileo, but discipline is not doctrine: even when the discipline is ordered directly by the Pope. Surely the disciplinary acts of the Inquisition, especially in such a famous case as Galileo, serve a teaching role, in a broad, sociological sense of teaching, but from a theological point of view such acts ought not to be confused with formal doctrinal pronouncements.

Although some theologians and some popes may have thought that it was heretical to embrace heliocentric astronomy, the *official* acts of the Church in 1616 and in the trial of Galileo in 1633 were disciplinary not doctrinal. The 1616 prohibition of books which espoused the new astronomy issued by the Index of Forbidden Books was gradually relaxed. The 1757 edition of the Catalogue of Forbidden Books did not include books that favoured heliocentric astronomy. In 1820, Pope Pius VII sanctioned the granting of the imprimatur to works presenting Copernican astronomy as true and not merely as hypothetical. The failure to change Church discipline more expeditiously did contribute, however, to the myth that there was a fundamental conflict between faith and science.

From History to the Legend of Warfare Between Science and Religion

The view that there has been a long history of warfare between science and religion really was nurtured in the 19th Century, the great age of positivism, which saw modern science as the pinnacle of human thought. For the positivists, science was objective, inductive, and experimental - and it was born in the great revolution of the 17th Century when geniuses such as Galileo and Newton succeeded in overthrowing the heritage of Aristotle. Thus, the Inquisition's treatment of Galileo was but one of the attempts to impede the inevitable progress of the human mind. The legend of Galileo's persecution by the Inquisition became part of the larger story - also widely accepted - of the Scientific Revolution. The more one saw that Revolution in terms of the victory of the modern scientific method, a method, so it was claimed, which Galileo pioneered, the more it was easy to accept what had become the common wisdom of the Inquisition's attempting to thwart scientific progress to protect the literal truth of the Bible. Such a view of the 'Galileo Affair' leads easily to the conclusion that science and religion are necessarily incompatible.

Warfare Between Science and Religion

Increasingly, the metaphor of warfare between science and religion served as a principle in the modern world's understanding of its own history and the legend of Galileo was important evidence for the purported truth of this interpretation. At the same time the legend has been held captive by this interpretation: so much so that, even today when we know how ill-founded the legend is, it remains difficult to reject it. This is particularly true in the United States where Andrew Dickson White's *History of the Warfare of Science with Theology in Christendom* (1896) enshrined what has come to be a historical orthodoxy difficult to dislodge. White used the example of the 'persecution' of Galileo by the Inquisition as an ideological tool in his attack on religious opponents of evolution. Since it was so obvious by the late 19th Century that Galileo was right, it was useful to see him as the great champion of science against the forces of dogmatic religion. White's account may sound a bit extreme; nevertheless, we should be able to recognise an affinity between it and the persisting legend of Galileo:

> [Galileo's] discoveries had clearly taken the Copernican theory out of the list of hypotheses, and had placed it before the world as a truth. Against him, then, the war was long and bitter. The supporters of what was called 'sound learning'

declared his discoveries deceptions and his
announcements blasphemy. Semi-scientific
professors, endeavoring to curry favor with the
church, attacked him with sham science; earnest
preachers attacked him with perverted scripture;
theologians, inquisitors, congregations of cardinals,
and at least two popes dealt with him, and, as was
supposed, silenced his impious doctrine forever...

The whole struggle to crush Galileo and to save him
would be amusing were it not fraught with evil.
There were intrigues and counter-intrigues, plots
and counter-plots, lying and spying; and in the
thickest of this seething, squabbling, screaming
mass of priests, bishops, archbishops, and cardinals,
appear two popes, Paul V and Urban VIII. It is most
suggestive to see in the crisis of the church, at the
tomb of the prince of the apostles, on the eve of the
greatest errors in church policy the world has
known, in all the intrigues and deliberations of these
consecrated leaders of the church, no more evidence
of the presence of the Holy Spirit than in the caucus
of New York politicians...

The Church as Obstacle to the Advancement of Man

The debate over papal infallibility, formally defined at the
First Vatican Council in 1870, as well as liberal reaction

to the Catholic Church's condemnation of 'modernism,' and the politics of the Italian Risorgimento only reinforced the skewed interpretation of the Galileo affair as a prime example of the hostility of the Catholic Church to reason and science. How, so it was alleged, could the Church proclaim its pontiff to be infallible when at least two popes affirmed as a matter of faith the false position that the Earth did not move? It was the same 'reactionary' Church which condemned Galileo, which also opposed Italian unification and modern political and social movements, and was, accordingly, a great obstacle to the advancement of man. It is interesting that in current debates about whether human cloning or embryonic stem cell research should be prohibited the spectre of Galileo is invoked by those who argue for freedom of scientific research and cast those who wish to prohibit such research as modern-day inquisitors.

Learning the Wrong Lesson

Current controversy within the Catholic Church concerning what kind of authority Rome has - or should exercise - on a range of topics also provides evidence for the enduring influence of the legend of Galileo. Hans Küng, for example, has argued that Pope John Paul II's "judgments on birth control and the ordination of women were as infallibly wrong as were those of his predecessors on astronomy and heliocentricity." Writing in the British Catholic weekly, *The Tablet*, in March 2004, Michael Hoskin of Cambridge University reflected on what he called "The Real Lesson of Galileo". He claimed that "the much heralded 'rehabilitation' of Galileo in 1992 was in part an attempt to gloss over the falsity of the doctrinal decrees issued - with papal endorsement - by the church organisations of Galileo's day. If the Holy Office was mistaken in its doctrinal decree then its successor, the Congregation for the Doctrine of the Faith, may sometimes be mistaken now. But this is not a conclusion the Church has allowed." Note how important it is for Hoskin that what happened in the 17th Century be recognised as an error in doctrine - versus what I called an error in discipline. According to Hoskin: "The real issue of the Galileo affair for the Church today - an acceptance of the possible reformability of doctrinal pronouncements promulgated by the Congregation for the Doctrine of the Faith even with the approval of the Pope - has yet to be learned."

Hoskin's interpretation is informed, in part, by the work of a Swiss-Italian historian, Francesco Beretta, who has done ground-breaking work in the recently opened archives of the Inquisition. Beretta claims that a censure of heresy was *formally* applied to heliocentric astronomy and since such a censure was pronounced by the pope, as supreme judge of the faith, it acquired the value of an act of the magisterium of the Church. He thinks that in 1633 Pope Urban VIII acted in his role as "supreme judge in matters of faith" and that already in 1616 Pope Paul V, in his formal capacity as head of the Inquisition, declared Copernican astronomy to be "contrary to Holy Scripture" and therefore cannot be defended or held. This latter decision was the basis of the order given to Galileo not to hold or defend the new astronomy. Any evaluation of Beretta's thesis requires careful distinctions both of different senses of heresy and of the judicial and magisterial authority exercised by popes.

Learning the Right Lesson

The rhetoric of the hostility between science and religion continues to exercise a powerful hold on contemporary interpretations of the history of the modern world. Since Galileo was correct in his conclusion that the Earth moves, it became and remains useful to portray defenders of other scientific claims as modern-day Galileos and to see their opponents as successors of the Inquisition. And, with respect to topics in bioethics, too often there has been a confusing or conflating of ethical and scientific theses. The condemnation of research on human embryonic stem cells, for example, is not a rejection of scientific knowledge; it concerns what actions are ethically legitimate, not what knowledge is somehow unacceptable.

In the front of his own copy of the *Dialogue Concerning the Two Chief World Systems*, Galileo wrote:

> Take care, theologians, that in wishing to make matters of faith of the propositions attendant on the motion and stillness of the Sun and the Earth, in time you probably risk the danger of condemning for heresy those who assert the Earth stands firm and the Sun moves; in time, I say, when sensately or necessarily it will be demonstrated that the Earth moves and the Sun stands still.

Here we find both Galileo's commitment to demonstrations in science, a commitment which he shares with Aristotle, and his admission that there is not yet such a demonstration for the motion of the Earth. The passage also reaffirms a key principle Galileo set forth in his *Letter to the Grand Duchess Christina*: that when investigating physical questions one should not begin with biblical texts. Galileo warns the theologians to avoid acting imprudently, lest they be faced with the unpleasant task of condemning as heretical those propositions which they now declare to be orthodox.

Faith and Science in Harmony

There is no evidence that, when Galileo acceded to the Inquisition's demand that he formally renounce the view that the Earth moves, he muttered under his breath, *eppur si muove*, "but still it moves". What continues to move, despite the historical evidence, is the legend of a fundamental conflict between science and religion. There was a conflict between Galileo and the Inquisition, but it was a conflict between those who shared common first principles about the nature of scientific truth and the complementarity between science and religion. In the absence of scientific knowledge that the Earth moves, Galileo was required to affirm that it did not. However unwise it was to insist on such a requirement, the Inquisition did not ask Galileo to choose between science and faith.

Further Research and Reading

http://Galileo.rice.edu

http://galileo.imss.firenze.it

Beretta, Francesco. *Galilée devant le Tribunal de l'Inquisition. Une relecteur des sources*.

Blackwell, Richard J. *Galileo, Bellarmine, and the Bible*.

Blackwell, Richard J. *Behind the Scenes at Galileo's Trial*.

Fantoli, Annibale. *Galileo: For Copernicanism and for the Church*.

Finocchiaro, Maurice A. (ed.). *The Galileo Affair: A Documentary History*.

Machamer, Peter (ed.). *The Cambridge Companion to Galileo*.

McMullin, Ernan (ed.). *The Church and Galileo*.

Shea, William and Mariano Artigas. *Galileo in Rome*.

What Science Says About God
The Reason Series

This DVD set, based on the award winning book *New Proofs for the Existence of God: Contributions of Contemporary Physics and Philosophy*, by Fr. Robert J. Spitzer, S.J., Ph.D. is aimed at high-school and college age students which explains the evidence for God from physics (along with the topics of evolution, the Bible vs. science, and aliens, etc.). The information is presented in a narrative form with the central character, a college student, defending his faith against a hostile atheistic roommate. Beautiful shots of Mt. Wilson Observatory and guest appearance from the Director of the Observatory.

Chance or Purpose?
Creation, Evolution, and a Rational Faith
Christoph Cardinal Schoenborn

Cardinal Christoph Schönborn's article on evolution and creation in *The New York Times* launched an international controversy. Critics charged him with biblical literalism and "creationism". *Chance or Purpose?* directly raises the philosophical and theological issues many scientists today overlook or ignore. The result is a vigorous, frank dialogue that acknowledges the respective insights of the philosopher, the theologian and the scientist, but which calls on them to listen and to learn from each another.